WITHDRAWN

PRINTED BY THE MURRAY PRINTING COMPANY, MASS.
BOUND BY H. WOLFF BOOK MFG. CO., INC., N.Y.

FOREWORD

ON THE DAY this is being written I had one of many long lunches with Charles Addams, in the course of which I introduced to him a man who, at a conservative estimate, is one of the most sophisticated persons on earth. The man is so urbane that he has his collars made at a Madison Avenue shop, wears them exactly once precisely, and throws them away. He wears in his necktie a pearl stickpin, which he does *not* throw away. The sleeves of his suits are so carefully tailor-made that I am surprised that any blood ever reaches his wrists. He knows all that is going on in the faubourgs of Paris, France, and can tell you what was going on there in 1905; he knew then, and he knows now, who was doing what to whom and for how much. The parties he has given, and the parties he has gone to, are fabulous. And curiously enough, the man is not a bum: he works for a living, has abundant self-respect, and his very job is so special that it is unique. With the possible exceptions of Michael Arlen and Michael Romanoff, I cannot think of a man in the world who is more a man of the world, with all of that term's implications.

This man—whom I shall call Muggsy Grogan—stopped at our table on his way out, and I introduced him to Addams, mentioning the first name. "Charles Addams the cartoonist?" said Muggsy. "I can't begin to tell you how much I've enjoyed your work." Couldn't begin, maybe, but he tried, he tried. And I give you my word, Muggsy had tears in his eyes.

"Who the hell was that?" said Addams, after Muggsy left.

Later in the day, when I got home, a five-year-old member of my household sat with me and looked at the drawings in *The New Yorker*. I explained, or attempted to explain, all the drawings but one. That one she merely looked at, smiled approvingly, and said, "Charley Addams." She and Addams are on a first-name basis.

Now, somewhere between the simple sophisticate and the blasé child are the millions of admiring, fascinated, sometimes mystified, often frightened Americans who are Addams fans. Some certified public accountant in the audience may want to point out that *The New Yorker* has nowhere near a million circulation and that Addams therefore cannot have millions of fans. My answer to that one is: "That's why you're an accountant, Bub, and I'm an author. I know more about people." I know that anyone who ever saw an Addams drawing is an Addams fan. I never have heard anyone groping for the name Addams when trying to identify an Addams drawing or, as happens every day, using the name in its by-word sense. There are plenty of Addams fans who have seen only an issue or two of *The New Yorker*, and I suspect that there are quite a few who haven't seen the magazine at all, but have Got the Idea through hearing other people say, "She's a regular Charles Addams," or "The house was a real Charles Addams." And there are others who see Addams' work because they are lucky enough to have a friend who proudly owns an Addams original.

The outstanding Addams collection that I know about is owned by Herbert Marshall, the distinguished British actor, who just incidentally could tell most Americans a lot of things about America. A long time ago, on my first visit to Bart Marshall's house, I was delighted to see the many drawings he had, and I went about enjoying myself. Later I said to Bart, who, by the way, draws very well himself, "But you haven't got my *favorite* Addams."

Bart looked at me a moment, then, without asking me to tell him which drawing, he said, "Dear John, come with me."

We went upstairs to his dressing room and, yes, by God, he had the picture.

I am not going to identify the drawing in this Foreword, because Charles Addams has worked so hard in the years since that afternoon at Marshall's that I no longer could have a single favorite. There was a time when he might have used my title for a collection of his drawings: *The De-Flowering of New England*, by Charles Addams. But nowadays he spreads himself, so that sometimes months go by without our seeing the famous Addams mansion and its jolly occupants. This is a good thing for all of us, just as, for instance, it was a good thing that Richard Rodgers did not stop writing music when he finished the score of *Oklahoma!*. In that connection, I would like to see Charles Addams branch out even more, specifically into theatrical design, and I don't know why Disney couldn't do at least one Addams a year.

In its overweening modesty, *The New Yorker* is unlikely ever to publish a profile of Charles Samuel Addams, so for the benefit of those who are not acquainted with Addams the Man, I shall provide a few facts. Addams the Man is, I may say, All Boy, if not exactly All American-Boy or Youth's-Companion. His outstanding sideline is the motor car, a hobby which at least partly explains why he has had to work so hard. At the moment of writing he has only two automobiles: an Austin saloon is one, and the other is a Mercedes-Benz, which he owns instead of a yacht. Any yacht shorter than one hundred and ten feet would cost him less than the Merc, but Addams does not like the illusion of speed he might get from a fast commuting boat. He just likes speed, plain. He occasionally participates in organized road races as a member of the Sports Car Club of America, but since these races are held at intervals of months, he frequently organizes his own races: Addams *vs.* all the cars on the road from New York City to Quogue, Long Island.

With the author of these words he shares a fondness for the institution of the Long Luncheon, not because it is Continentally fashionable, with a parade of fancy dishes and delicate wines, but because if you sit down at one o'clock, you can be finished your liver and bacon by a quarter to two and can stay there, watching the Powers models, and taking in good Scotch whiskey until half past six, by which time the Powers models are back again, and it is too late to do any work that day. (Promptly at six-thirty, it should be mentioned, we are joined by Mrs. A and Mrs. O'H, former models and model wives.)

Addams is a big man, about 6′1″ and around 195, a toxophilist who can handle a sixty-pound pull, but I don't think he'd hurt a fly. I never have seen him lose his temper, although that is not to say he doesn't get mad. He happens to be what is called easygoing, and has a decent contempt for the opinions of mankind. He speaks with a New Jersey twang plus a drawl of his own, and but for the grace of God, which gave him his enormous talent, his sense of humor, and his impatience with banality, he might have become a successful politician. (I suppose I am made conscious of that danger by the knowledge that his father's middle name was Huey.)

It may reveal something of the nature of the man to report that he and Mrs. Addams have a black toy poodle called Tulip. If the analysts can get anything out of that, they're welcome to it. But I can't imagine a man who owns a dog named Tulip cutting off his own or anyone else's ear.

—JOHN O'HARA

Princeton, New Jersey
April, 1950

"*We've never believed in allowances. They have to earn every cent of their pocket money.*"

4

Water Shortage

"Isn't it wonderful to think that we'll always have this record of their golden childhood days?"

"Aw, come on, Marilyn. You can be Ingrid Bergman."

1

2

3

4

5

6

7

8

9

10

11

12

"In addition to refusing to cultivate any wholesome interest in group activities, he is perverse, crafty, and wanton in those in which he does engage. These are, I feel impelled to emphasize, far beyond the outcroppings of normal juvenile mischief; in fact, they are the early evidences of what may be an extraordinarily morbid ingenuity. I have gone to such length in describing the situation because I know that you will want to be thoroughly informed of the facts."

"All right, children, creative play period is over!"

"Come along, children—time for your nap."

"Now for the human side of the news."

"Don't you carry the large economy size?"

"Darling!"

"Oh, darling, can you step out for a moment?"

"Goodness, Murray, it wouldn't be a picnic without ants."

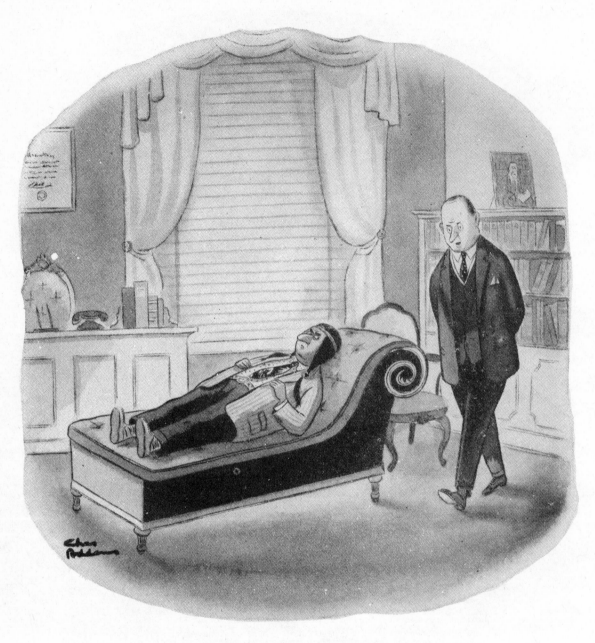

"*I think we're getting somewhere, Mr. Great Cloud Shadow. Your neurosis apparently stems from a submerged resentment against your ancestors for disposing of Manhattan Island for only twenty-four dollars.*"

"Ours is a very old family."

"For heaven's sake, can't you do anything right?"

"*Oh, I like missionary, all right, but missionary doesn't like me.*"

"*Ready, dear?*"

"George! George! Drop the keys!"

"You will go to the hall closet. You will get your hat. You will get your purse. You will walk to your neighborhood grocer and you will take advantage of our special offer of three boxes of Sampson's Egg Noodles for the price you ordinarily pay for two. You will go to the hall closet . . ."

48

"You know, sometimes I can't help wondering if Mr. Lawrence really <u>did</u> go to Chicago."

"*When you hear the signal, the time will be one-thirty-four and one half.*"

"Goddam suction disks jammed again!"

"*You're in a strange mood today, I must say.*"

"You needn't wrap it. I'll ride it home."

"*Dearest: How I wish you were here with me now to see how lovely our little garden has become! The black nightshade is in full bloom, and the death camass we planted last fall is coming along beautifully. The henbane seems to have shot up overnight. You will be glad to know that the dwarf's hair was not affected by the dry spell, as we feared, after all. A myriad delightful little slugs have appeared, as if from nowhere, on the rotten stump by the belladonna patch, and this morning I noticed snake eggs hatching near the pool. Do finish up that business, darling, and hurry home.*"

"This is Uncle Zander. Grandfather always called him the black sheep."

"*Is that Mother, dear?*"

"*Bothered me a bit, too, at first, until I discovered they were real.*"

"*Do you, Oliver Jordan III, take this woman to be your lawful wedded wife?*"

"*It may be none of my business, but there hasn't been a train over that line in eight years.*"

"*Now, remember, you can have him as long as you feed him and take good care of him. When you don't, back he goes.*"

"Parker! You're letting him get the upper hand!"

"... and then I disconnected the booster from the Electro-Snuggie Blanket and put him in the deep-freeze. In the morning, I defrosted him and ran him through the Handi Home Slicer and then the Jiffy Burger Grind, and after that I fed him down the Dispose-All. Then I washed my clothes in the Bendix, tidied up the kitchen, and went to a movie."

"*Looks like old Burton decided to take it with him.*"

"You'll see, chicks, that half the fun is in making it yourself."

"*Now, don't come crawling back asking me to forgive you.*"

"Now kick Daddy good night and run along to bed."